Call Me Grandpa

A Man's Wish for His Grandchild

WRITTEN BY

Jerry Pociask

ILLUSTRATED BY

Marsha Grill

To my children:
Jason and his wife Lindsay, Jessica and Catherine,
incredible people in their own right

and

to my sister Chris,
for all of her help and patience.

My shallow, deliberate breathing was broken with the shrill ringing of the phone. Afternoon naps were becoming more the norm and I found myself enjoying that sleep. Half sitting, half laying in my old chair, forgetting to turn off the phone, the chirping sound startled me. I answered partially asleep.

"Hello?"

"Hello, Grandpa!"

"Oh, hello. HUH?" I fought the fogginess still in my head.

It was bound to happen sooner or later, but now with a still heavy mind the words didn't hit.

"I said Helllllllo, G R A N D P A!!!"

How is it possible that in life we anticipate certain events and yet when they occur we are never prepared?

That now more familiar push of emotions got in the way as my words tried to escape.

"How wonderful." I was choking back tears.

"Yep...It's official! You're going to be a grandpa!"

"So tell me everything!"

"What's the due date?"

"Is everything ok?"

"Do you want a boy or a girl?"

"How are you feeling?"

"What about work?"

"Do you have enough money?"

"Do you need anything?"

"What can I do?"

"Nothing, we are all set. But there is one question."

"What's that?"

"Do you prefer being called Grandfather, Poppy or Gramps?"

"Call me Grandpa."

Tears etched their way across the expanse of cracked and craggy skin. Years ago those tears would have streaked downward without hesitation. Today they channeled across wrinkled cheeks, routed by lines constructing small canals and diverting their travel every which way.

"That is absolutely wonderful!"

"You know how much I love you," I whispered.

"I love you, too."

I reached across and hung up the phone.

That night, sleep was elusive. Were afternoon naps interfering with my sleep? Pulling myself from the warm covers and stumbling toward the back door, I pulled on my old parka. Arguing with the jammed zipper it was easier leaving the jacket open against the crisp night. The snow creaked as I stepped off against the now frozen ground. The cold night didn't feel cold even as my breath fogged my glasses. Casey romped along, always ready for the chance to be free.

The stars sparkled against a deep sky. I felt I could reach up and take one down and save it in my pocket. The moon was already almost down. The quiet amplified my deep breaths. Ice crystals clung to tiny hairs above cracked lips. It seemed lately more breaths were needed to get across this land. The two of us stood in the middle of winter stubble, Casey at rest against my right leg. We searched the night sky. She sensed something was up.

"Grandpa," I whispered.

Casey's wet nose found warmth in the palm of my hand held at my side. Instinctively she knew. Those tears froze in the lines etched in my face. New ones melted and then replaced old.

I marveled at the mystery above me. Each star was an energy unto its own. Wondering which star had breathed its energy into my grandchild, I began to pray…

"Dear Lord!

Please make my grandchild perfect in every way! Ten toes and ten fingers, two eyes and two ears, these will be the first things I will look for. Bestow a voice that rivals that of your finest songbird to bring joy to anyone who hears that soft sweet music. Allow peace and happiness, love and joy so as to never understand heartache and in no way allow the experience of evils men have wrought on your earth. Breathe in a sense of justice to never know prejudice. Allow talents to be bestowed and become a benefit in all corners of your earth. I ask this in your name, Oh Lord. Amen."

I stood motionless, self-satisfied that my prayers were heard. Casey scratched her neck unaware of the secret deal I had just made.

"Silly fool!"…the silence was invaded by an intruder.

"HUH?"

Eyes moved about searching for who had snuck up on me.

"I said, silly fool."

Casey was looking at the sky, wagging her tail while I searched the landscape to put a face with that voice.

"Why am I a silly fool?" My voice blasted the hushed night.

"You ask for much, that's why."

Still unsure my eyes searched the gray woods….

"I asked for health and happiness for my grandchild. Is that too much to ask for?"

"Yes."

"Why?"

"You are my son. Did you always have health and happiness?"

"Your Son?" I hesitated. "Well. No. Not always."

"And did it matter?"

"At times it did! Who is this, anyway?"

"Did you live through it all? Any regrets?" said the voice ignoring my question.

"Regrets? No. Given the choices I had then and knowing what I did? I would have to make all the same choices!"

"Did I ever once leave your side?"

"No…I didn't think so."

"And your children, were they always perfect? Did you not worry about them from time to time?"

"Of course I did! There were times I never knew what could happen!"

"And did YOU ever leave their side?"

"NEVER would I do that!"

"Oh, they were punished when necessary, but I wouldn't ever leave them when they needed help."

"Then why do you ask for so much for your grandchild?"

"I don't want my grandchild to suffer!"

"But did your suffering not make you a stronger man? Did you not face life's challenges straight on, doing what you felt was best?"

"Yes. Yes, I guess I did."

"And did you not at times want to give up and feel as if there were no use in going on?"

"Yes."

"Yet I never left you."

"And your children, did your heart not break when their first love went unreturned? Did you not feel their pain as they grew past all of that to become the caring and compassionate people they are?"

"Yes."

"And so did I...so did I. You ask for the wrong things of me. Do you see?"

"Then what is it I should ask for?"

"*You must ask that your grandchild learn
the same lessons that I taught you and in return you taught your children.*"

"What lessons?"

"*Oh, you old, old man...*"

"I'm tired."

The voice appeared to resonate from the woods. Maybe in front of me I thought, still trying to see who was there.

"*We are all tired but your purpose is not yet done. So listen again so that you can be a reminder to your children and guide them as I have guided you.*

I offer a set of values that has carried man through all of time. Since the time of Adam, I have asked you to follow these guidelines. Some have; many have not. But let us begin."

"Learn to live your life as a whole and not for yourself. Self-focus is the one cause of sadness. It makes us think we suffer from want or need. We live our lives in fear instead of love. When we focus on others, we give of ourselves and are assured that others will in turn give to us. When we learn we are a part of a greater whole our spirit becomes magnificent."

"Always remember that today IS a good day. Man can easily look back and judge what was. He can never look forward and judge what could be. All he can do is consider his actions now, today, and know who he is. Remember that today is a good day. Promise yourself to live each and every day one moment at a time. Savor life. Live life."

"*Recognize everything happens in the right time and the right place. People think if they work longer, harder or faster they will get ahead. Yet the world is full of people who have worked harder, longer and faster than you and don't have what you have. We must come to this understanding; you will get what you are to have when the time is right. Life does not occur on your terms.*"

"You should have already been taught this one, old man," the voice assumed, with a chuckle.

"Respect age. There is a difference between intelligence and wisdom. Intelligence is a tool people use in life; wisdom is the product of that life. See those people who go ahead of you as having been where you wish to be. See them as someone who you may draw great strength from. See each as having the wisdom of time behind them."

"Be of value to others. Did I not teach you in lesson one to learn to share with others? Then you must also learn to take what others have to offer you. When we accept a gift from someone, we honor that person. We honor their abilities by sharing their thoughts and ideas instead of competing for attention. By allowing others to enter our lives we become thoroughly enriched. When someone gives you a compliment they are saying they admire you. Say 'thank you.' Otherwise you belittle who they are.

Patience must be cultivated and appreciated. This is a desirable quality to manage. We can ask for much and it may or may not be given. There is a season to all things. Can we plant a seed and force it to grow? No! There is a process to life. The seed will be planted. The sun will shine upon the earth and warm it. We water the earth and it in turn warms and nurtures that seed. Do we not accept these things as natural law? Then we must see patience as part of natural law and accept that all comes at the right time and the right place."

"Did I not give you but one mouth and two ears? Then for number seven I will grant you the one mouth and the two ears you have asked for. But I give this gift to your grandchild as a lesson. One mouth and two ears mean they are to listen twice as much as they should speak.

When you speak, you are too busy trying to give your own opinion. What you have to say falls on deaf ears. Listening allows you to hear and understand what others want you to know. We honor their wisdom by listening to them.

Stop along the way and listen to the undemanding things in life. The wind tap tapping a branch against a window or the rain as it runs across the sidewalk. The sun as it warms the earth or the sound of your lover's heart beat."

"The next is perhaps the most difficult to learn. When we acquire possessions, we wish to protect them. We are afraid to give up or give away that which we see ourselves as having worked so hard for. Instead, we save and store our belongings for years, content in our own beliefs. It is only decades later after we pass, our children crawl into attics and inside garages to see things they could have used long ago, now rotted and torn, nibbled by mice that benefited from our selfishness. What more can we need than to have a warm house, clothes to cover ourselves and enough food to keep us alive? What of those who have none of that? Would it not be of great help with one warm blanket we may have given them? Would they not have been grateful for even one night to have gone to bed satisfied instead of lying awake to the sound of a complaining stomach?

Once a year take inventory of your life. Keep nothing beyond one year. If you haven't used an item in that one year, you probably will never use it again. Think of how valuable it may be in the hands of someone who will."

"You have learned the next lesson well. Living in accord with all things is lesson number nine. Do you remember when you shot that sparrow with your pellet gun and how you cried afterwards wondering if he or she had small babies? You realized then that your actions affected another being. So it is with anything we do. As with the 'right time and the right place' everything happens with a purpose. When we refuse to live in accord with life, we stop the forces that are in place to create the perfect outcome. When a pebble is dropped into an unruffled lake it creates ripples that pulse across the entire lake. Those first ripples are apparent, and then slowly, they disappear. Unconsciously, those ripples move across the lake toward the distant shore and move the smallest grain of sand. That beach will never be the way it once was from such an imperceptible change.

Our own actions in life are like that stone tossed into the lake. They will ripple across time finding their way to forever change another's life. We must be aware of the possible outcomes of our actions. We must learn to live in accord with others."

"This brings me to number ten,
the great wonder of life.

I never understand why you expend
so much time and energy trying to
define who I am when in reality I am
everyone. You sit in church on Sunday
professing your beliefs in me and yet
deny my presence in others. Did I not
say that man was created in my image?
Do you not believe that I am omnipotent?
Then how can you deny your own omnipotence? You waste energy trying to prove my very
existence when I am all around you! Did you doubt who I was the first time you felt the tiny
little hand of your child wrapped around your fingertip? Did you doubt my existence when you
gratefully saw your mother's suffering end in her passing? Then why do you deny me now?
Look around you and see the skeptics. They sit and judge you by your actions. Is that who
you wish to be judged by? By whose standards would you prefer to live?"

"Now, don't be so self-righteous in your view of yourself. Even though you may see Me in everything does not give you the right to preach. You always needed a reminder of the next guideline. Patience came easier to you than did modesty. But you learned. You all learn in time. You saw the advantage of living as an assembly, operating as a whole rather than only interested in yourself. For a while you wanted all the attention. When you didn't get it you didn't like it. That lesson made you stronger and it made you stronger in not only my eyes but the eyes of your children. They could see a man who wasn't always right, someone who was willing to stand for what he believed and able to be thankful for his blessings. In your own humility your children learned a great lesson.

In their lesson you achieved the greatest tribute ever given a man."

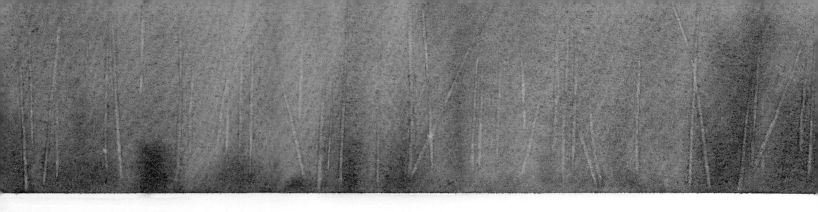

"For in your humility you bent a knee to something greater than yourself. You saw that regardless of who you were or where you were, there was always something you could count on. And that something was Me. Yes, I have loved you since the day I placed you in the sky. Since the time I ignited your energy and allowed you to shine upon this earth you were destined for greatness. You spent an earth's lifetime in lessons and have learned them well. You have made Me a part of your life and the lives of all whose hearts you have touched. No person who has met you will ever travel without an understanding of what it is like to be loved by Me.

And so now I give you your reward."

"*I give you a grandchild!*

With ten toes and ten fingers, two eyes and yes two ears and a mouth, everything will be given to become a great and wondrous human being. The same light I gave to you I will give to this child. Stars have shone for eons and one is about to be brought to earth as your grandchild.

To your children I make this promise. I promise they will see and experience all that you have as a parent. All that you rejoiced over and all that you have suffered will be theirs. For it was in your living that you became a man. And as a man, your greatest reward comes with your grandchild. You will see yourself again as a child. You will live your life as if it was a movie, and then you will understand why I cannot grant your prayer."

And with that the voice was gone.

Slowly the cold air made its way back into my bones. The pain in my hip was back.

"Dunno, what do ya think, Case?" I chuckled to myself and wondered what someone would have thought seeing me carrying on a conversation with the night. Casey lumbered by my side, content to know she was going back in. Warm air thawed frosty hands and face when the back door was pulled open.

I thought about what the voice had said and then I thought about my own children. All of them had become great in their own ways.

What parent wouldn't be more proud?

The jammed zipper slid about an inch, insistent on being stuck. The worn collar rested on the bare peg next to the door. A hand steadied me as I kicked off well-oiled leather boots. My mind raced trying to make some sense of it all…my prayer…the answers given to me…the events of my life were all planned to be part of my children's lives…those were the lessons I had to learn…then I knew…

…I knew what it means to be called…Grandpa!

Life Management, LLC